No Sweat Paragraphs

Simple and Logical Strategies for Teaching Children to Write

No Sweat Paragraphs: Simple and Logical Strategies for Teaching Children to Write
Copyright © Carol Pirog 2020
Anchor Book Press
440 W Colfax Street, Unit 1132
Palatine, IL 60078
ISBN: 9781949109412

Printed in the United States
Cover Art by Dusan Pavlic
Animals on Paragraph Pages by Kid Games

Parents unable to buy this book may contact Anchor Bool Press, Ltd to request a PDF that can be reproduced. Send request to Carol at anchorbookpress@gmail.com

No Sweat Paragraphs

Simple and Logical Strategies for Teaching Children to Write

Carol Pirog

Anchor Book Press • Palatine

Table of Contents

Setting the Foundation

There are many different programs for teaching children to write. This program teaches children how to write a basic paragraph. Older children can also do the Five-Paragraph Essay lessons. This program is based on getting the most progress out of the least amount of time. Whether you are a parent or a teacher, there are many other things you can do besides spending excess time teaching something that can be done more quickly. This program is designed in a simple and logical way to avoid wasting your time and your children's time. In addition, it is created with the research-based strategy of providing individual feedback on each assignment. Many children struggle with writing and other subjects because the class moves on before they have mastered the foundational concepts, and no one realizes they need help.

Once a child has mastered the concept of writing a basic paragraph, he or she can move on the Better Sentences sections which is the basis for building a better paragraph. Your child will use the more complex sentences to begin writing better paragraphs. The main idea of this program is the child learns to write a basic paragraph before moving on to a great paragraph. It may seem you can do both at once, but laying foundational skills is essential. When too many skills are being worked on at the same time, it takes longer for most children to master the assignment than learning the skills independently and building on a strong foundation.

The **key** to your child's success using this program is to **make corrections**. I'm sure you have heard the saying, "Practice makes perfect." However, that is only true if what is practiced is perfect. If you are not doing something correctly, all practice will do is ingrain the incorrect way to do it. Making corrections helps your child to practice perfectly. Almost as important as correcting mistakes is to **avoid power struggles**. When a child engages in a power struggle, the goal is to win, not make the choice that is best. See section at the back of the book if you need more information on avoiding power struggles. A well-known, but rarely mentioned fact, is if a child is not engaged in the lesson, it does not matter how good the lesson is the child will not learn. A power struggle greatly reduces the chance that your child will engage in the lesson, even if he or she completes the work.

There are a few essential points you need to remember for this program:
1. Try to make it fun. Some children just do not like to write, and nothing will make it fun. To make it a little less of a chore, give them a choice. If they don't want to write about animals, let them pick something else – superheroes, TV shows, video games, sports, cars, singers – just about anything will work. Give them an incentive, activities and time together work best. Something like, when you are finished here, let's go for a bike ride or let's read a book. You know your child. Pick things he or she would like to do either with you or alone. While some parents feel children should just do what they need to, remember the goal. The goal is for your child to learn to write, not a platform to build character. Because as important as building character is, it can be accomplished in other ways without making it more difficult to teach writing. A good book that talks more about this concept is *Parents REACH for Success* (or *REACH for Success* for teachers)by Belinda Adams.

2. Writing is important as it triggers areas of the brain that control memory. Writing a paragraph helps your child learn focus and organizational skills. When your child gets to college, this will be a foundational skill not only for assignments but for remembering information in an organized fashion.

3. People learn from mistakes. The program is set up for students to correct mistakes. Correcting mistakes does two things. First, it has the child practice the right way of doing something. Second, it encourages more effort. This is especially true as the child becomes proficient. I always tell students if they only have one or two mistakes, they can make the corrections by erasing rather than having to rewrite the paragraph. I have found this to be one of the most effective incentives to encourage quality work.

4. Children learn to read more easily when they read their own writing, be sure to take advantage of this fact by having your child read what he or she writes. Many children will enjoy adding a cover and stapling all the pages together to make a book which they can read to you or a sibling.

Set Up

If you spend a little bit of time to prep, you will find that daily lessons are less time consuming for you and for your child. The first thing to do is make writing folders – one for you and one for your child or each student you are working with. For you, a pocket folder works best. Put lessons that have not been done on one side and completed lessons on the other. You will need the completed lessons again if your child does the essays or wants to make a book. A manila folder works great for kids. Through the years I have found most kids enjoy decorating the front of their folder. Before they do, write _____'s Writing Folder across the top, preferably in marker. Near the end the book you will find words for writing. Copy these. If you only have a printer, take a picture and print that. If you do not have a copier or folder, write the words on a sheet of paper and glue or tape to construction paper or cardstock. Be resourceful – the idea is to have a tool for your child to begin the process of becoming more independent in their learning. The blank section at the end is for your child to write words they want to remember that are not on the list. If you find your child is continually misspelling a word or asking you how to spell the same word, add it to the list. As your child writes, encourage him or her to look up words in their writing folder if they don't know how to spell them.

Next copy the lesson for the day or the week. This book is a black-line master. Meaning that you have permission to copy pages for you own children or students. Each lesson is meant to be used twice. Once as a fiction paragraph about the whimsical animal in the picture. After that, as a nonfiction paragraph/mini research project about the animal. If you desire, you can also use the lesson a third time after you child has completed the Better Sentences section.

You are finished with the prep work and ready to begin the lessons.

Writing Paragraphs

The idea behind this program is students write simples sentences to build a solid foundation when they first start writing paragraphs. Rather than worry about complex sentence structure, students concentrate on the mechanics of writing a paragraph. This is one reason that parents fill in the essential words box, so that students concentrate on the paragraph, not spelling words which they have not learned yet. Note: I know that some say not to worry about spelling. However, my opinion is that it instills bad habits and reinforces poor spelling. It is so simple to provide the support that lets a child practice correctly. Building skills on a solid concept that has been mastered is a strategy that most students find helpful with any new skill. While writing, students should make the connection between what they have written and reading. To do that, have student read the paragraph when they have finished writing. Young children should point to each word as they read to help them make the connection that the printed text is the words they are saying and it represents the writer's ideas, rather than just memorizing what they have written. If he or she is having difficulty, point to the words for the child.

The first two lessons have examples on the left side page and the student page is on the right. Depending on your child's level of writing, you can go through the example with him or her or just use it as a guide for yourself. After the first 2 lessons, the left-hand page is the organizer for older students, who will be writing smaller letters and longer sentences. The right-hand side is for younger students. In the lesson, your child is writing a basic paragraph with a topic sentence, three detail sentences, and a concluding sentence. (If your child has difficulty writing sentences, do the Basic Sentence Section before starting paragraphs – the time will be worth the effort.) Instruction in writing a paragraph assumes a child can write a basic sentence, starting with a capital letter, ending with a period. Child should also be able to form most letters and group the letters in words together with space between each word. There is a printing section, if help is needed in that area.

*Topic Sentence – explain to child this should be something general, not a detail. The example says, "This is Pete the Parrot." This sentence is based on the title of the paragraph and the picture. It could also be something like, "Parrots are interesting birds." Or, "Parrots are beautiful birds."
*Three Detail Sentences – The organizer gives some clues to help children think of details and to stay on topic. For Pete, the paragraph tells what he looks like, what he eats, what he does. Then it creates a sentence for each. One of the foundational skills of writing a paragraph is to stay on topic. In this general paragraph, anything about parrots works as long as it isn't so general that it could be the topic sentence.
*Conclusion – For a conclusion, the paragraph uses a general sentence with feelings – I love Pete the Parrot. Something like, "I wish I had a parrot," or "Parrots are great birds," could also be used.

Day 1

Step 1: Fill out organizer – parent fills in essential words, child will need to know how to spell. Student completes the rest of the organizer (top part of the page). As a parent or teacher, you need to gauge how much support the child needs. On the first day, you should at least talk though what the child is thinking.

Step 2: Write paragraph on lines. Be sure to explain about indenting the first word if your child has not learned this skill, yet. Remind child to start all sentences with a capital and end with a period. Make sure child starts next sentence at the end of the last word of the previous sentence. (Some students want to start a new line for every sentence – explain that is a list, not a paragraph.)

Step 3: Have your child read the paragraph to you.

Step 4: You correct the paragraph. Use a blue pen so that corrections are easily seen. Check for these things: A – paragraph is indented and the first word on each new line starts at the beginning of the line; B – letters are legible with spaces between words; C – Letters are written on lines; D – Every sentence starts with a capital and begins on the same line as the last word in the previous sentence; E – every sentence ends with a period; F – all words are spelled correctly. To make corrections do the following: If there is no space between 2 words, draw an arrow to point it out. If a capital is missing, cross out lowercase letter and write a capital above it. If a word is misspelled, cross it out and write the correct spelling above it. **Note:** If your child has lots of mistakes, pick one or two to focus on; don't try to correct everything at once. If there are too many corrections, it is too difficult for a child to remember them all. If there are a lot of mistakes at the sentence level, do the Basic Sentence lessons before continuing.

Day 2

Step 1: Have your child rewrite the paragraph on the lines below the first paragraph. If there are not enough lines use a plain sheet of lined paper. The first few times, sit with your child to be sure that the corrections are made. Some children balk at making corrections. Try not to make this a power struggle. Explain two facts about rewriting. First, making corrections helps you learn. Second, even authors who make lots of money by writing books have to rewrite everything.

Nonfiction Writing

Once you child has written all ten paragraphs, start over and write the paragraphs as nonfiction. As a parent/child project, google an animal. Find a short description of the animal. Help your child pick 3 facts. Then write a paragraph about the animal. Get your child in the habit of giving credit for information. For example, "Google says parrots eat …" You are not looking for APA style citations, just teaching the concept that if you use someone else's information, you have to give them credit. Talk about the first paragraph and how it was their ideas. If you are feeling like a teachable moment, explain about intellectual property.

If you think that your child is still struggling with a basic paragraph, use the blank pages to do more basic paragraphs. Find pictures in magazines or on the internet or have your child draw a picture to write about. Branch out to other things besides animals – community helpers, careers, transportation, superheroes, movie or book characters. Whatever your child is interested in will make the perfect topic.

Sentence Writing

This section is comprised of 2 parts. The first part is the basic sentence section for children just starting to write, or children struggling with writing a correct simple sentence. The second is writing more complex sentences.

Remember, children learn from their mistakes. You should correct all sentences. At this level correct everything. If your child is making a lot of mistakes, do not do the whole page in one day. Instead, do just one sentence per day. If letter formation is an issue, glue or tape a chart to the back of the writing folder that shows how to write all the letters. You can use the one in this book or search the internet for an image that shows the correct way to form letters – complete with a dot for the starting point and arrows that show the direction to go. Setting the foundation of correct letter formation will help later when your child is learning cursive. Corrections:

A. All sentences start on the left end of the line.
B. There are spaces between words, but not between letters in the same word.
C. Letter formation is acceptable/readable and basically on the line.
D. First letter is a capital, names are capitalized, and a period at the end.
E. Words are spelled correctly (you should write down words your child can't spell so the he or she can copy them correctly). This is not a spelling lesson but writing triggers memory. You do not want your child to 'practice' spelling a word incorrectly.
F. You might be asking is it necessary to require all of this from a young child. The answer is yes. The biggest reason for lack of progress in the public school is the teacher just does not have the time in a class of 25 students to make sure everyone is doing it correctly. Therefore, some students develop habits that are hard to break. You have the advantage of having just one or maybe a 2 or 3., but not 25. Help your children develop a firm foundation for higher learning.
G. I can't emphasize this enough – when making corrections do it in the spirit of, 'everyone makes mistakes and correcting mistakes is how we learn.' It always helps to share some of your mistakes, especially something that can be laughed at if your child is resistant correcting mistakes. Something along the lines of, "I remember when..."

Basic Sentences

It is pretty basic, no pun intended. The lesson has the child writing a simple sentence with a sentence starter. I can see …, or John can see …, etc.

Step 1: Go over the directions and the example with your child.

Step 2: Depending on your child's achievement level, it might be a good idea to discuss the sentence he or she will write. If your child is at the basic sentence level, do not expect a lot of independent work. Time spent now will allow your child to build on a strong foundation later. Note: Your child can use the name of any person in the sentence.

Step 3: Child writes sentence on the first line.

Step 4: You make the corrections (don't just mark something wrong, write it correctly (cross on a lowercase t and write and capital T above it) because the child will be copying the right way on the next line. Use arrows to indicate there should be a space between words. This is called scaffolding – providing increased or decreasing levels of support so your child can move up to the next skill level and independence level.

Step 5: Sit with your child to make sure that he or she rewrites the sentence correctly.

Note: This assignment should take 10 or 15 minutes. Monitor you child as they write the first sentence. If it takes 10 minutes, only do 1 sentence today. If it doesn't take that long, but there are many corrections, only do 1 sentence today. If your child makes mistakes when copying the corrected sentence, for future sentence corrections, sit with the child and make sure the sentences are correct, using cues and reminders as necessary.

Note: On day one, have the child do one sentence and then correct it before going to the next sentence. Some corrections will be made to the second sentence the first time it is written. For example, rather than your child writing 3 sentences with no capitals or periods, correct the first sentence. On the second sentence, cue child if necessary (don't forget the period). On subsequent days, you can decide whether to do 1 sentence or a whole page at a time.

Blank form.

If your child enjoys writing, use this as an everyday fun activity.

If your child did not master writing sentences with the 3 basic sentences sheets, use this for extra practice, as many days as needed to master the basic sentence.

Step 1: Get a picture. Everyone likes choices. Let your child choose the picture. You can print pictures from the internet, cut pictures out of magazines or old coloring books, or draw stick figures. If this takes a long time, try to have your child do the picture the day before as a fun activity. This can be motivating for a child who likes to draw. If your child does not like to draw, use one of the other options.

Step2: Repeat instructions from above. There are only 2 sentences on these pages so there is more room for the picture.

Better Sentences

This is for the older student who is still writing a basic sentence or the younger child who loves writing and the children who have mastered the Basic Paragraph section. Some children need help to figure out sentence structure and how to expand their thoughts in writing. Even students who talk well, sometimes have difficulty when it comes to putting their thoughts on paper. Therefore, this is a formula type writing that will help the child get past the difficulty they are having when it comes to putting thoughts on paper.

Step 1: Go over directions with your child (at least the first day).
Step 2: Discuss options.
Step 3: Your child writes sentences.
Step 4: You make corrections.
Step 5: Your child rewrites sentences correctly.
Note: Students who do not like to write might need some extra incentive. It is better to get one correct sentence than a lot of poorly written sentences. With older children who do not like to write, I usually tell them if they only have 1 mistake, they do not have to rewrite the sentence (unless it is the capital or period).

Another incentive might be to make the first sentence serious and the second sentence funny. Read the funny sentences at dinner time or some other family time.

The key to remember is to try to make it fun or at least have an incentive that makes it worthwhile.

Writing Essays

This section for students who have mastered writing a great paragraph with complex sentences. A child in 3rd grade who loves to write, could do well writing essays, but generally speaking essay writing is for students who are in 4 grade or above. Again, this can be a basic essay with simple sentences if your child is older but struggles with writing.

This eases the child into writing by using the paragraphs already written in the Paragraph Writing Section. The lesson is on writing a 5-paragraph essay – an introductory paragraph, 3 detail paragraphs (that are already written) and a concluding paragraph.

Day 1: The first essay is my favorite animals. Child completes the organizer. Introduction should have at least 2 complex sentences or 3 shorter sentences. My intro will go something like this: I love going to the zoo to see the animals. (Simple sentence option - I love animals.) My three favorite animals are _____, _____, and _____. (Be sure to teach child about commas for a list if he or she has not learned that yet.) For the body (detail paragraphs) child should write name of animal on the line. My conclusion might go something like this: I hope to go to the zoo soon. I want to see the _____, _____, and _____.
Day 2: Child writes essay, copying the detail paragraphs he or she has already written.
Day 3: Child brainstorms to come up with ideas for future essays. Parent or teacher corrects essay. As before, write in proper spelling, capitals, or punctuation.
Day 4: Child rewrites essay.

Essay ideas for future writing:
My favorite foods, shows, sports, etc.
The weirdest looking animals, plants, buildings, etc. (google these)
Community helpers, occupations, etc.
Important people in history, science, education
Topics from social studies or science

"I write to discover what I know."
Flannery O'Connor

Lesson Plans

Some parents have said that they are not used to scheduling lessons. So, this is a basic weekly lesson plan for each section. Follow the one that you are using for your child.

Basic Paragraphs				
Monday	Tuesday	Wednesday	Thursday	Friday
Write 1 basic paragraph. Read paragraph to parent or sibling.	Make corrections. Read paragraph to someone.	Write 1 basic paragraph. Read paragraph to parent or sibling.	Make corrections. Read paragraph to someone.	Write in a journal about the best thing that happened this week. Read to someone.

Basic Sentences				
Monday	Tuesday	Wednesday	Thursday	Friday
Write sentence and make corrections. (Parent decides how many sentences.)	Write sentence and make corrections. (Parent decides how many sentences.)	Write sentence and make corrections. (Parent decides how many sentences.)	Write sentence and make corrections. (Parent decides how many sentences.)	Write in a journal about the best thing that happened this week. Read to someone.

Better Sentences				
Monday	Tuesday	Wednesday	Thursday	Friday
Write sentence and make corrections. (Parent decides how many sentences.)	Write sentence and make corrections. (Parent decides how many sentences.)	Write sentence and make corrections. (Parent decides how many sentences.)	Write sentence and make corrections. (Parent decides how many sentences.)	Write in a journal about the best thing that happened this week. Read to someone.

Printing				
Monday	Tuesday	Wednesday	Thursday	Friday
Practice writing letters. Make corrections as you go.	Practice writing letters. Make corrections as you go.	Practice writing letters. Make corrections as you go.	Practice writing letters. Make corrections as you go.	Write in a journal about the best thing that happened this week. Read to someone.

Essays				
Monday	Tuesday	Wednesday	Thursday	Friday
Complete Organizer	Write Essay	Brainstorm Writing Ideas	Rewrite Essay	Journal-read to someone

Pete the Parrot

My Ideas	Essential Words
Looks Like **green and yellow**	crackers
Eats **crackers**	fly
Does **fly**	

Draw a Parrot, of you want to.

___This is Pete the Parrot. He is green and yellow. He eats crackers every day. He likes to fly. I love Pete the Parrot.

_____

_____

_____

_____

Name:

_____

My Ideas	Essential Words
Looks Like _____	_____
	_____
Eats _____	_____
Does _____	_____

Draw a lion.

_____

_____

_____

_____

_____

_____

_____

_____

Name:

The Armadillo

My Ideas		Essential Words
Looks Like shell		shell
		destroy
Eats bugs		interesting
Does destroys the grass		

Draw an armadillo.

_____Armadillos are interesting animals. They have a hard shell. Armadillos like to eat bugs. They will destroy the grass. I do not want a pet armadillo.

Name:

_____

My Ideas	Essential Words
Looks Like _____	_____
	_____
Eats _____	_____
	_____
Does _____	
Draw an armadillo.	

_____

_____

_____

_____

_____

_____

_____

_____

Name:

_____

My Ideas	Essential Words
_____	_____
_____	_____
_____	_____
Draw	

_____

_____

_____

_____

_____

_____

_____

_____

_____

_____

_____

Name:

_____

My Ideas	Essential Words
Looks Like _____	_____
	_____
Eats _____	_____
	_____
Does _____	
Draw	

_____

_____

_____

_____

_____

_____

_____

Name:

My Ideas

_____

_____

_____

_____

Essential Words

_____

_____

_____

Draw

Name:

_____

My Ideas	Essential Words
Looks Like _____	_____
	_____
Eats _____	_____
	_____
Does _____	
Draw	

_____

_____

_____

_____

_____

_____

_____

Name:

_____

My Ideas	Essential Words
_____ _____ _____	_____ _____ _____

Draw	
	_____

_____

_____

_____

_____

_____

_____

_____

_____

_____

_____

_____

_____

_____

Name:

My Ideas	Essential Words
Looks Like _____	_____
	_____
Eats _____	_____
	_____
Does _____	
Draw	

_____

_____

_____

_____

_____

_____

_____

_____

_____

Name:

My Ideas	Essential Words

Draw	

Name:

_____

My Ideas	Essential Words
Looks Like _____	_____
	_____
Eats _____	_____
	_____
Does _____	
Draw	
	_____

_____

_____

_____

_____

_____

_____

_____

Name:

_____

My Ideas	Essential Words
_____	
_____	_____
_____	_____
	_____

Draw	

_____

_____

_____

_____

_____

_____

_____

_____

_____

_____

_____

Name:

_____

My Ideas	Essential Words
Looks Like _____	_____
	_____
Eats _____	_____
	_____
Does _____	
Draw	

_____

_____

_____

_____

_____

_____

_____

Name:

_____

My Ideas	Essential Words
_____	_____
_____	_____
_____	_____
Draw	
	_____

_____

_____

_____

_____

_____

_____

_____

_____

_____

_____

_____

Name:

_____

My Ideas	Essential Words
Looks Like _____	_____
	_____
Eats _____	_____
	_____
Does _____	
Draw	

_____

_____

_____

_____

_____

_____

_____

_____

Name:

_____

My Ideas	Essential Words
_____	_____
_____	_____
_____	_____

Draw

_____

_____

_____

_____

_____

_____

_____

_____

_____

_____

_____

_____

Name:

_____

My Ideas	Essential Words
Looks Like _____	_____
	_____
Eats _____	_____
	_____
Does _____	
Draw	
	_____

_____

_____

_____

_____

_____

_____

_____

_____

Name:

_____

My Ideas	Essential Words
_____ _____ _____	_____ _____ _____
Draw	

_____
_____
_____
_____
_____
_____
_____

_____
_____
_____
_____
_____
_____

Name:

_____

My Ideas	Essential Words
Looks Like _____	_____
	_____
Eats _____	_____
	_____
Does _____	
Draw	_____

_____

_____

_____

_____

_____

_____

_____

Name:

My Ideas

Essential Words

Draw

Name:

_____

My Ideas	Essential Words
Looks Like	_____
	_____
Eats	_____
	_____
Does	

Draw

_____

_____

_____

_____

_____

_____

_____

Writing Basic Sentences 1

Directions: Write a sentence about the things you see.

If you made some mistakes, write sentence correctly on 2nd line.

Remember: Sentences start with a capital and end with a period.

Example: Mary sees 2 dogs.

Word Box
cats   bunny   ducks one   two   three

_____

_____

_____

_____

_____

_____

Writing Basic Sentences 2

Directions: Write a sentence about the things you like to eat.

If you made some mistakes, rewrite sentence correctly on 2nd line.

Remember: Sentences start with a capital and end with a period.

Example: John likes to eat popcorn.

Word Box
apples   ice cream   cake

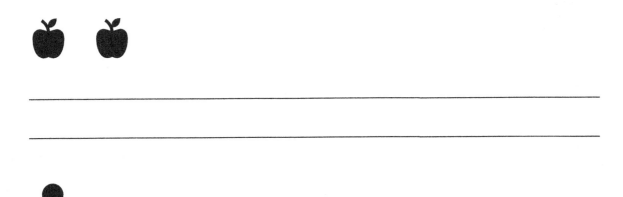

Writing Basic Sentences 3

Directions: Write a sentence about the things you like to do.
If you made mistakes, rewrite the sentence correctly on the 2nd line.
Remember: Sentences start with a capital and end with a period.

Example: Sue likes to paint.

Word Box
swim   ride bikes   dance

_____

_____

_____

_____

_____

_____

Writing Basic Sentences 4

Directions: Choose a picture and write a sentence.

If you made mistakes, rewrite the sentence correctly on the 2nd line.

Remember: Sentences start with a capital and end with a period.

Example: I can read books.

Word Box

_____

_____

_____

_____

Better Sentences 1

Directions: Turn these sentences into better sentences.
If you made mistakes, rewrite sentence correctly on the 2nd line.
Tell more: Describe, When, How, Where

Example: John has a dog.
Better: John has a little brown dog at the park.
Better: John has a cuddly dog in his lap.

Mary has a cat.

_____

_____

The phone rang.

_____

_____

Better Sentences 2

Directions: Turn these sentences into better sentences.
If you made mistakes, rewrite sentence correctly on the 2nd line.
Tell more: Describe, When, How, Where

Example: John has a dog.
Better: John has a little brown dog at the park.
Better: John has a cuddly dog in his lap.

The rabbit jumped.

_____

_____

The boy fell.

_____

_____

Better Sentences 3

Directions: Turn these sentences into better sentences.
If you made mistakes, rewrite sentence correctly on the 2nd line.
Tell more: Describe, When, How, Where

Example: John has a dog.
Better: John has a little brown dog at the park.
Better: John has a cuddly dog in his lap.

The girl laughed.

_____

_____

The tiger ran.

_____

_____

Better Sentences 4

Directions: Turn these sentences into better sentences.
If you made mistakes, rewrite sentence correctly on the 2nd line.
Tell more: Describe, When, How, Where

Example: John has a dog.
Better: John has a little brown dog at the park.
Better: John has a cuddly dog in his lap.

_____

_____

_____

_____

_____

_____

Directions: Write a five-paragraph essay on your favorite animals with an introduction, 3 detail paragraphs (use the ones you already wrote) and a conclusion. Fill out organize, then write essay on notebook paper.

Don't forget transition words for paragraphs 2, 3 4, and 5. Always use a comma after a transition word.

Transition Words
next then first second third finally in conclusion

Title:	
Introduction	_____ _____ _____ _____
Detail Paragraph 1	_____ _____ _____ _____ _____
Detail Paragraph 2	_____ _____ _____ _____ _____
Detain Paragraph 3	_____ _____ _____ _____ _____
Conclusion	_____ _____ _____

Directions: Write a five-paragraph essay about the funniest animals with an introduction, 3 detail paragraphs (use the ones you already wrote) and a conclusion. Fill out organize, then write essay on notebook paper.

Don't forget transition words for paragraphs 2, 3 4, and 5. Always use a comma after a transition word.

Transition Words
next   then   first   second   third   finally   in conclusion

Title:	
Introduction	_____ _____ _____
Detail Paragraph 1	_____ _____ _____ _____ _____
Detail Paragraph 2	_____ _____ _____ _____ _____
Detain Paragraph 3	_____ _____ _____ _____ _____
Conclusion	_____ _____ _____

Directions: Write a five-paragraph essay on your favorite sports with an introduction, 3 detail paragraphssc and a conclusion. Fill out organize, then write essay on notebook paper.

Don't forget transition words for paragraphs 2, 3 4, and 5. Always use a comma after a transition word.

Transition Words
next   then   first   second   third   finally   in conclusion

Title:	
Introduction	_____ _____ _____ _____
Detail Paragraph 1	_____ _____ _____ _____ _____
Detail Paragraph 2	_____ _____ _____ _____ _____
Detain Paragraph 3	_____ _____ _____ _____ _____
Conclusion	_____ _____ _____ _____

Directions: Write a five-paragraph essay on community helpers with an introduction, 3 detail paragraphs and a conclusion. Fill out organize, then write essay on notebook paper.

Don't forget transition words for paragraphs 2, 3 4, and 5. Always use a comma after a transition word.

Transition Words
next   then   first   second   third   finally   in conclusion

Title:	
Introduction	_____ _____ _____
Detail Paragraph 1	_____ _____ _____ _____
Detail Paragraph 2	_____ _____ _____ _____
Detain Paragraph 3	_____ _____ _____ _____
Conclusion	_____ _____ _____

My Words for Writing				
about	because	call	each	give
after	before	could	every	go
again	big			going
all	boy		find	great
any	but	day	for	
ask	by	do	from	
at		did	funny	
had	if	let	need	people
has	in	live	no	please
her	is			put
high			of	
him	jump	man	old	
house	just	many	once	
how		mine	open	
	know		over	
right	take	use	walk	yes
round	thank		want	you
	the	very	went	your
should	them		were	
some	then		what	
stop	thing		when	
	think		who	
			will	
			with	
			work	
			would	

More Writing Words		
black	1 one	11 eleven
blue	2 two	12 twelve
brown	3 three	13 thirteen
grey	4 four	14 fourteen
green	5 five	15 fifteen
orange	6 six	16 sixteen
pink	7 seven	17 seventeen
purple	8 eight	18 eighteen
red	9 nine	19 nineteen
white	10 ten	20 twenty
yellow		100 hundred

Word Family Words for Writing

-ad	-ake	-all	-am	-an
bad	bake	ball	bam	can
dad	cake	call	ham	Dan
had	Jake	fall	jam	fan
lad	lake	hall	Pam	man
mad	make	mall	ram	pan
pad	rake	tall	Sam	ran
sad	take	wall		van

-and	-ap	-at	-ay	ear
band	cap	bat	day	beat
hand	gap	cat	hay	heat
land	lap	fat	Jay	meat
stand	map	hat	may	seat
	nap	mat	pay	
	rap	rat	say	
	tap	sat	way	

-ell	-en	-est	-ight	-ill
bell	Ben	best	fight	Bill
fell	hen	nest	light	fill
sell	men	pest	might	hill
tell	pen	rest	right	pill
well	ten	test	tight	will

-ing	-ip	-oat	-og	-ook
bring	dip	boat	dog	book
ding	rip	coat	hog	cook
ring	sip	goat	log	look
sting	tip			took

-op	-ug	-ump	-un	
hop	bug	bump	bun	
mop	hug	dump	fun	
stop	rug	jump	run	
top	tug	pump	sun	

My Own Writing Words

_____	_____	_____
_____	_____	_____
_____	_____	_____
_____	_____	_____
_____	_____	_____
_____	_____	_____
_____	_____	_____
_____	_____	_____
_____	_____	_____
_____	_____	_____
_____	_____	_____

Printing

Directions: Trace the letters or words, write letter of words on the line below.

a   a   a   a   a

_____

_____

c   c   c   c   c

_____

_____

t   t   t   t   t

_____

_____

a   cat   a   cat

_____

_____

Printing

Directions: Trace the letters or words, write letter of words on the line below.

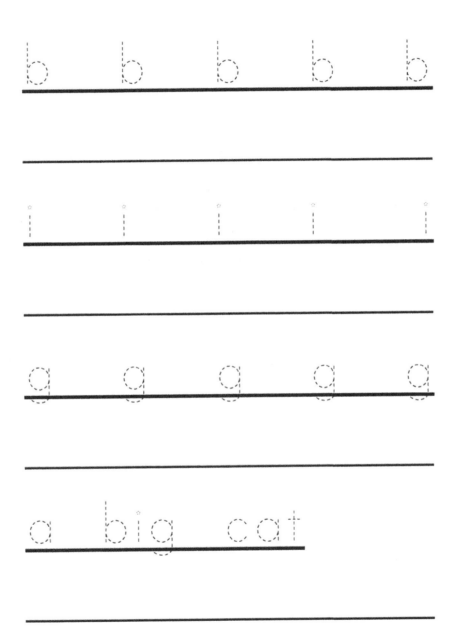

Printing

Directions: Trace the letters or words, write letter of words on the line below.

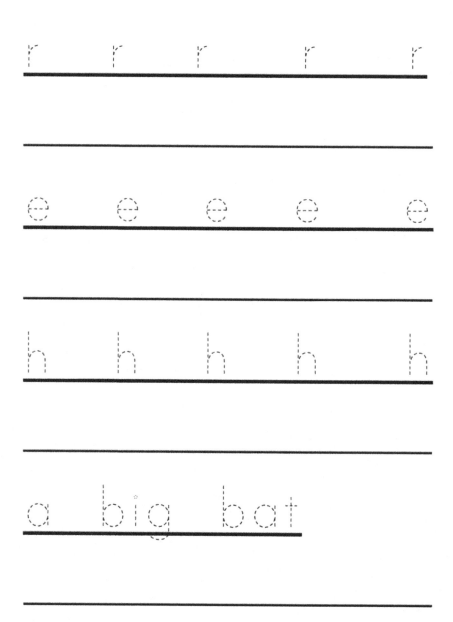

r   r   r   r   r   r

e   e   e   e   e

h   h   h   h   h

a big bat

Printing

Directions: Trace the letters or words, write letter of words on the line below.

Printing

Directions: Trace the letters or words, write letter of words on the line below.

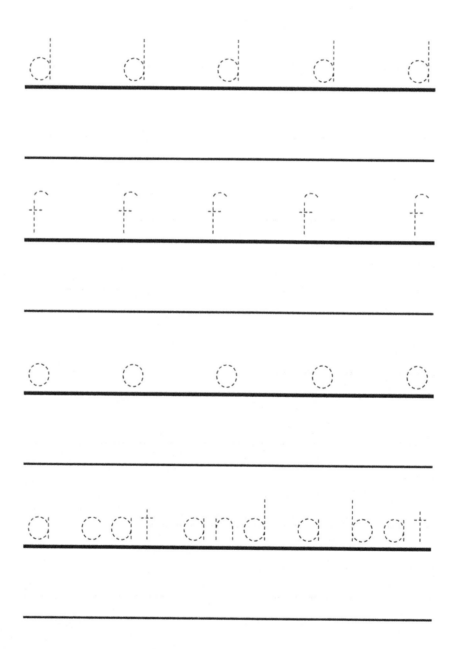

d   d   d   d   d

_____

_____

f   f   f   f   f

_____

_____

o   o   o   o   o

_____

_____

a cat and a bat

_____

_____

Printing

Directions: Trace the letters or words, write letter of words on the line below.

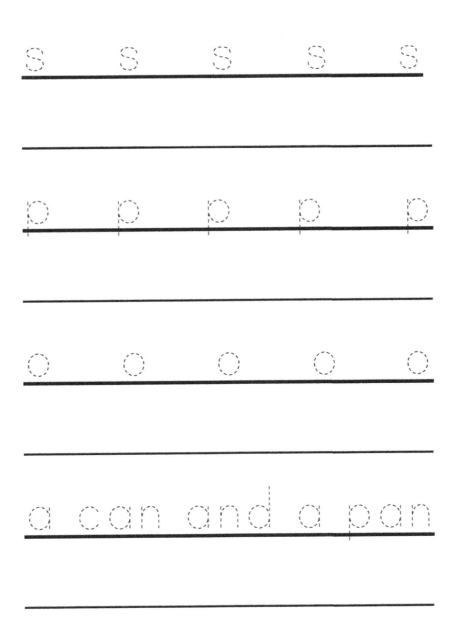

s   s   s   s   s

_____

_____

p   p   p   p   p

_____

_____

o   o   o   o   o

_____

_____

a can and a pan

_____

_____

Printing

Directions: Trace the letters or words, write letter of words on the line below.

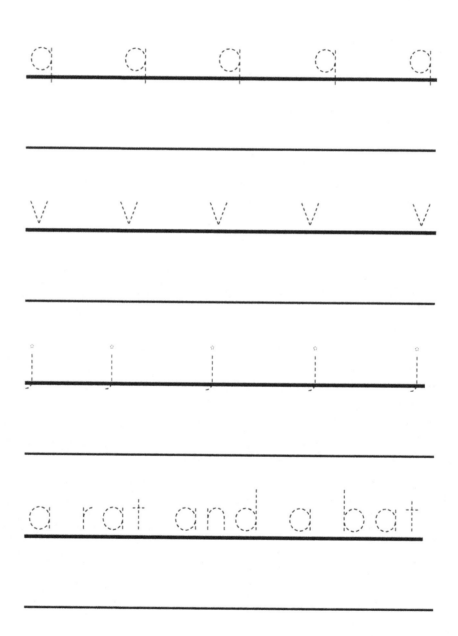

Printing

Directions: Trace the letters or words, write letter of words on the line below.

U   U   U   U   U

_____

_____

W   W   W   W   W

_____

_____

X   X   X   X   X

_____

_____

up and down

_____

_____

Printing

Directions: Trace the letters or words, write letter of words on the line below.

m   m   m   m   m
_____

_____

y   y   y   y   y
_____

_____

z   z   z   z   z
_____

_____

more cats
_____

_____

Printing

Directions: Trace the letters or words, write letter of words on the line below.

k   k   k   k   k

_____

_____

I will work fast.

_____

The van is red.

_____

Do not quit yet.

_____

Printing

Directions: Trace the words, write words on the line below.

Go find the bat.

_____

See a dog jump.

_____

I play the sax.

_____

A cat ran home.

_____

A a　B b　C c　D d　E e

F f　G g　H h　I i　J j　K k

L l　M m　N n　O o　P p

Q q　R r　S s　T t　U u　V v

W w　X x　Y y　Z z

"No one is perfect. That's why pencils have erasers."

Unknown

Writing Games

You will have to decide for your family which is best, cooperative games or competitive games. Most of the games can be played either way. Not everything needs to be written. Part of the idea of the game is to get children thinking about possibilities. Often, the difficulty with writing is not knowing what to write.

Family Fun:
Every person needs a pencil and piece of paper or marker and white board; one timer.
Pick a word family – it is best to start with something easy like -at or -an.
Set timer for one minute. Everyone writes as many words as they can.
Take turns with each person reading their words (don't skip this – builds reading skills).
Everyone picks one word to use in a sentence (written or spoken).
Competitive: Person with the most words wins.
Cooperative: Play two rounds and everyone tries to beat their first round.

Build a Sentence:
Prep – Ahead of time write 10 sentences on 3 x 5 cards, one word per card. Be sure the sentences are easy enough for the youngest player to read or play with partners. Be sure to use capitals and periods.
Shuffle all the cards. Lay face down in the center.
First player takes a card and lays it face up. Continue with each person drawing 1 card on their turn.
Competitive: The first person to make a sentence wins the game. if no one has a sentence by time the cards run out, have each player return half of their cards to the bottom of the pile (player chooses which cards to return). Shuffle and keep going.
Cooperative: Keep playing to everyone has a sentence.

Sentence Foundations:
Prep – choose basic 3 or 4-word sentences. Write on strips of paper.
Decide on the rules ahead of time. Will the sentences have to be possible or can they be imaginative, like "The blue Cow jumped over the new moon on Monday." (Basic sentence, "The cow jumped.")
Shuffle the sentences and put in the center.
First player takes a sentence and reads it to everyone.
Starting with the person that drew, each person writes or tells a better sentence.
Competitive: Longest sentence wins or players vote for best sentence.
Cooperative: Everyone picks their favorite sentence.

Remember, competition can be fun, and some children thrive on competition. You determine which is best for your family. If you use competition, choose rules that allow everyone to win sometimes. It is not fun if you always lose.

Power Struggles

There are many books on power struggles. Three of my favorite books are *Parenting (or Teaching) with Love and Logic* by Foster Cline and Jim Fay; *Boundaries for Kids* by Henry Cloud and John Townsend; and *Parents REACH for Success* by Belinda Adams. As discussed in the books in more detail, the fundamental idea is that in a power struggle, no one wins. This is because each person is making decisions based on what will help them to win the power struggle, not what is best.

In my experience, the key to avoiding power struggles is choice and how things are said. For example, if I say to my student, you are going to stay in for recess if you do not complete the assignment, the child feels he has no choice. Right away, he starts figuring out how to keep me from making him do the assignment, not how to get the assignment done. The truth in life is it is very difficult to make anyone do anything if they decide they will not do it no matter what the consequence. What I need to remember, my goal is to get the assignment done, not prove that I can make the child do the assignment or that I can make him sorry if he doesn't by punishing him.

What is the better choice? I say to the child, you can go to recess when you are finished (or watch a movie or play a video game or ride your bike). It is up to you what you choose to do (be sure it is something the child will want to do and be willing to work for). Here I am telling the child it is his choice to do the assignment or not. There is really no difference, but you haven't set up the power struggle. A vital thing I need to remember is that I have to be ok with either choice. Maybe the student will stay in for recess two or three days, but sooner or later he gets the idea. Some of you may be doubtful, but I have taught for many years and it never fails. Eventually, the child realizes that it works better for him if he does the assignment. I don't scream and holler or tell the student he is wasting my time because I have to supervise him during lunch. If I do, he will know that I am not ok with his choice and he has won by inconveniencing me.

I also need to be sure the assignment is something the student can do, or I need to offer her support. For example, I might say that you can go to recess when you are done with the assignment. Let me know if there is any way I can help you. In working with a child this way, it helps the child learn that his or her actions have an impact on his life. A sense of some control gives the child incentive to figure out what works best for him, not how to win the fight. This also helps convey the idea that their choices matter. What happens next depends on the choice that is made. This is a very vital lesson for children to learn.

Keys:
1. Offer a choice – You can make those corrections now so we can go outside. Or you can stay inside if that works better for you and do the corrections then. (Do not allow child to move on to something that is more fun. It is ok to do chores first, but not play video games or watch TV.)

2. Offer support if it is needed – It is not good parenting to hold a child accountable for something they are unable to accomplish.
3. Accept the choice – Only give choices you are ok with. Do not tell the child we can go swimming when you are finished if you have been looking forward to going to the pool all week. It will be very difficult to accept his choice to skip the pool. Kids seem to have a sixth sense about knowing this kind of information.

Differentiation

No Sweat Paragraphs is the perfect book to help students at any achievement level. Struggling students or students with an IEP will benefit from these strategies with just a few modifications. The key is to remember the goal. While many strategies for struggling students just allow the student to do less work and learn less, the philosophy of this book is what can be done to help the struggling student be successful.

Explicit Instruction: Research has shown that struggling students are more successful when taught explicitly. What that means is tell the student how and why something is done rather than expecting the student to figure it out. One idea is to talk about what the student is going to write. For example. The organizer for Pete the Parrot has crackers written for what Pete eats. For the struggling student, you might need to prompt the student by asking him how to put that in a sentence – He likes to eat crackers.

Practice: Research has also shown that struggling students often need to practice more times before they master the skill. In the paragraph section, that could mean that you talk though the student's thought process for 5 or 6 paragraphs, instead of the first 2 or 3. It may also mean doing more than 10 paragraphs. As adults we tend to want to move on to bigger and better things. However, the stronger the foundation, the more support it will provide when you do get to those bigger and better things.

Encouragement: Experience has shown me that many struggling students feel defeated. They have failed so often they don't think they can – period. It doesn't really matter what the task is, they are sure they can't do it. You job is to convince them otherwise. One strategy I use with students is to talk about how everyone learns differently. I tell them they can learn when they are taught the way they learn best. Another, strategy is to use scaffolding. This is starting out with a high level of support and gradually decreasing the support as it is not needed. In the beginning you may need to sit with the student while he writes, giving cues as he or she proceeds. As the student becomes more proficient, you still sit with student, but give less and less cues until the student completes the task independently. Praise also goes in the section but be sure the praise is genuine. It is better to praise effort than accomplishment because it is hard work that you want to encourage. Effort is what will make the difference. With explicit instruction and effort, the student will accomplish more than he ever thought possible.
If your child struggles, sometimes it is helpful to mention your own struggles. Something like, I know how you feel. Last month my boss asked me to do something that was really a challenge for me. I had to ask others for help to figure out how to do it. Or, I remember when I was in the 4th grade, I thought I was never going to learn how to ___ (fill in the blank). Grandma had to help me every night until I finally figured it out.

"Writing is full of possibilities."
Anonymous

Summing It All Up

There is no need to waste time teaching things the hard way. A popular strategy in education is discovery learning. At times this may be beneficial, but it takes way more time that explicitly teaching a concept. Why do that when explicit instruction is faster and research shows it helps even struggling students. Be respectful of your child's time and your own time. Corrections are important. It is how children, and adults, learn the right way to do things and it provides motivation to put forth the effort needed to do things correctly

Avoid power struggles, no one wins. If you would like more information, look for *Parenting with Love and Logic, Boundaries with Kids,* and *Parents REACH for Success.* These books are great parenting resources that will help you navigate you way through many complex parenting issues.

Provide the support you child needs. Gradually reduce the level of support as your child becomes more and more proficient and it is not needed. Youi have heard, "Nothing succeeds like success." This is true because success gives people the courage to try more difficult things. Therein lies the basis for the self-fulfilling prophecy – my effort is based on the degree that I think I can do it. Why waste time and energy on something I cannot do? Help your child develop the courage to do difficult things.

"Whether you think you can or think you can't, you're right."

Henry Ford

Other Books by Carol Pirog

Common Core and Multiplication Facts

A blackline master that helps students learn multiplication facts and understand the process of multiplication. This book uses the math standards for multiplication, which are the same whether you are using Common Core or not. Knowing and understanding multiplication facts is the basis for higher math. Without this knowledge, students will continue to struggle in math as they get older.

Common Core and Addition Facts

A blackline master for younger students that helps students learn addition facts and understand the process of addition. This book uses the math standards for addition, which are the same whether you are using Common Core or not.

Surviving Common Core Math

This book was written to help parents who are struggling with Common Core. It explains common misconceptions surrounding Common Core. The author shares what parents need to know to help their children be successful in math without destroying the parent-child relationship.

Made in the USA
Monee, IL
03 August 2020